Acknowledgements

Once again, we would like to say a huge thank you to all of our students wno nave tried and tested the questions that follow in this book. As always, we are very grateful for your helpful feedback!

We'd also like to thank Emma Jolly and Luke Wheeler for all their enthusiasm and support in the office, as well as Mike Patteson, who we would simply be lost without!

We hope you find this book useful and challenging, and we wish you every success in your Verbal Reasoning exams. Good luck!

Charlie Boad and Kate Bridges, 2010

Books in this series:

11+ Verbal Reasoning Preparation Questions (Book One)
11+ Verbal Reasoning Revision Questions (Book Two)

www.luckygecko.com

Published by Lucky Gecko

© Lucky Gecko 2010

11+ Verbal Reasoning
Multiple Choice Revision Questions

Book Two

Charlie Boad and Kate Bridges

Useful Information for Parents

Verbal Reasoning is used across the country in numerous 11+, Common Entrance and Secondary School Selection tests.

This book is the second in our series and provides excellent revision for some of the most commonly used question types. It is most effective to test students' speed and accuracy under timed conditions.

It is therefore recommended that students work towards the time target indicated for each type so that they can fully appreciate the pace expected of them in Verbal Reasoning exams.

If you would like to ensure a firm foundation in each type before introducing timed conditions, we recommend you use the first book in our series, **'11+ Verbal Reasoning Preparation Questions' (Book One)** before moving onto this set of questions.

In this book, questions are presented in multiple choice format, and all answers should be marked clearly on the answer sheets provided. If your child is taking a multiple choice exam, it is worth noting that answers are often marked by a computer which looks for an appropriate pattern of pencil marks in the boxes provided. For this reason, it is important that they don't show any working out on the answer sheets, and that they mark their answers clearly for each question. Failure to do so may result in the answer being marked incorrect. For the same reason, it is also important that your child gets into the habit of using a pencil, so that they can easily change or erase answers.

According to standard practice for Verbal Reasoning, questions that require two answers must be completely correct to gain the mark - half marks are never awarded.

On each page, we have included a 'Rate This Type' star, which is for the student to colour in either red, orange or green once they have completed the set of questions. This is designed to help the student or parent easily identify the areas of strength and weakness so that further revision can be as focussed as possible.

We hope you find this book useful and we wish your child every success in their exams.

We do more than just Verbal Reasoning... to find out more about our small, friendly tuition company, please visit us at **www.luckygecko.com** .

Our resident geckoes are always busily working on new books, so keep checking the website to see our whole collection.

Hello from Lucky Gecko!

Welcome to our Verbal Reasoning Revision book. We hope you like it!

Please fill in some information about yourself.

This book belongs to _____

My school _____

My favourite subject _____

My favourite film _____

Draw a picture of yourself here

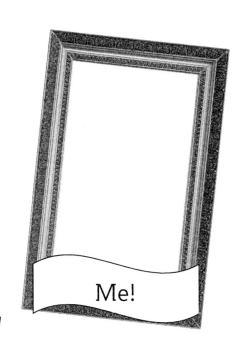

Me!

Read me!

In this book you will find 21 different types of questions.

We have included a star at the end of each type, which we would like you to colour in. Choose either **red**, **orange** or **green** once you have completed each set of questions to show how you feel about them. Be as honest as you can when picking your colour - it will help you see where you need to improve.

Here is a guide to help you choose:

	Red	I really didn't like this type. It was one of my least favourites and I found them very tricky.
	Orange	I didn't mind this type too much. It isn't my favourite but I felt I could work through them fairly confidently.
	Green	I really liked this type! It is one of my favourites and I felt happy and confident doing all of the questions.

Remember...

Some really helpful tips

* Make sure you mark your answers clearly and don't do **ANY** working out on the answer sheet - it's for answers only!

* Be careful to **MARK THE RIGHT NUMBER OF ANSWERS** down for each question. Some questions only need one answer, while others need two. If you put down the wrong number, you'll lose the mark.

* **DON'T PANIC!!** If you start to feel stressed, take a deep breath and do your best to relax. You can't concentrate properly if you're worrying!

Letter Sequences

Find the next two letters in each sequence and mark them on the answer sheet. The alphabet has been provided to help you.

A B C D E F G H I J K L M N O P Q R S T U V W X Y Z

For example: AC   BD   CE   DF   EG   **FH**

1.   CH, EF, GD, IB, KZ

2.   RD, OA, LX, IU, FR

3.   FW, GV, IU, LT, PS

4.   BX, GC, LH, QM, VR

5.   JU, GW, DY, AA, XC

6.   RG, NC, JY, FU, BQ

7.   FB, IF, LJ, ON, RR

8.   ML, NM, QP, VU, CB

9.   ZS, VW, RA, NE, JI

10. VI, CP, JW, QD, XK

11. HM, KH, OC, RX, VS

12. CB, CF, EJ, EN, GR, GV

Your colour rating....

Question 1		Question 2		Question 3		Question 4		Question 5		Question 6	
MQ	☐	DO	☐	YR	☐	BW	☐	VG	☐	XN	☐
MX	☐	DM	☐	US	☐	ZY	☐	UE	☐	HS	☐
NY	☐	HW	☐	UR	☐	AV	☐	AJ	☐	XM	☐
NS	☐	CN	☐	VR	☐	ZW	☐	GR	☐	IB	☐
XM	☐	CO	☐	GX	☐	AW	☐	VI	☐	NT	☐

Question 7		Question 8		Question 9		Question 10		Question 11		Question 12	
UV	☐	LJ	☐	GM	☐	ES	☐	YN	☐	IA	☐
OZ	☐	KK	☐	EL	☐	QS	☐	ZN	☐	KZ	☐
YX	☐	LK	☐	FM	☐	ER	☐	TS	☐	IZ	☐
YV	☐	TJ	☐	NE	☐	DR	☐	VH	☐	ZH	☐
DV	☐	ML	☐	FN	☐	ZY	☐	VN	☐	KV	☐

Time Target:
9 minutes

Time Taken _____

Your score....

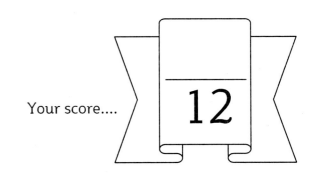

$\dfrac{}{12}$

Letter Analogies

In each question below, find the two letters that will best complete the sentence and mark them on the answer sheet. The alphabet has been provided to help you..

A B C D E F G H I J K L M N O P Q R S T U V W X Y Z

For example: AC is to BD, as CI is to **DJ**

1.   EI is to HJ, as PD is to _____

2.   BC is to ZE, as QT is to _____

3.   XH is to AL, as SY is to _____

4.   BY is to CW, as HU is to _____

5.   GL is to HG, as KA is to _____

6.   MO is to EQ, as CH is to _____

7.   ZE is to AV, as VR is to _____

8.   FF is to LZ, as WW is to _____

9.   HM is to SN, as DF is to _____

10.   TR is to QO, as EC is to _____

11.   EX is to GA, as QU is to _____

12.   HW is to PE, as CA is to _____

Your colour rating....

Question 1	
RE	☐
MC	☐
SE	☐
WX	☐
SF	☐

Question 2	
OV	☐
NV	☐
OX	☐
PY	☐
CF	☐

Question 3	
TB	☐
DC	☐
NQ	☐
VC	☐
PZ	☐

Question 4	
US	☐
IS	☐
IF	☐
JS	☐
BE	☐

Question 5	
MG	☐
FB	☐
JF	☐
LF	☐
LV	☐

Question 6	
UJ	☐
KJ	☐
UK	☐
XS	☐
JT	☐

Question 7	
WE	☐
RS	☐
EF	☐
IK	☐
EI	☐

Question 8	
DQ	☐
DR	☐
CQ	☐
CP	☐
EN	☐

Question 9	
WU	☐
IG	☐
HH	☐
IF	☐
WV	☐

Question 10	
BZ	☐
BA	☐
CA	☐
MI	☐
BD	☐

Question 11	
SX	☐
RX	☐
SY	☐
NH	☐
JH	☐

Question 12	
FW	☐
KI	☐
JI	☐
LK	☐
SH	☐

Time Target:
6 minutes

Time Taken _____

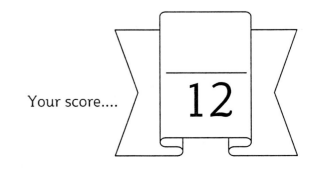

Your score....

12

Code Words

In each of the following questions, words have been written in code. You must work out the word
code which will complete the sentence and mark it on the answer sheet provided. The alphabet h
been given to help you.

A B C D E F G H I J K L M N O P Q R S T U V W X Y Z

For example: If the code for KIND is LJOE,
                        what is the code for TYPE?   **UZQF**

1.   If the code for TIRED is VKTGF

     what is the code for SLEEPY?

2.   If ORYXPW means ROBUST

     what does PWRUAB mean?

3.   If the code for ASCEND is ZHXVMW

     what is the code for HEIGHT?

4.   If NOMVIBZ means STRANGE

     what is the code for BIZARRE?

5.   If FPLSGYW means GROWLED

     what is does LYAJZML mean?

6.   If the code for CHANGED is GDEJKAH

     what is the code for AMENDS?

7.   If OHWWLU means HAPPEN

     what dos VJJBYZ mean?

8.   If the code for STRAIN is QPLSYB

     what does PAUUX mean?

9.   If the code for LOOKED is OLLPVW

     what does SFMTIB mean?

10.   If NRFLJ means IMAGE,

     what is the code for SLIDE?

11.   If the code for WRITE is XUJWF,

     what is the code for SCRIBE?

12.   If the code for CREAM is WLYUG

     what does MCABM mean?

Your colour rating....

10

Question 1	
QJCCNW	☐
UNHHSA	☐
UNGGRA	☐
VNGHRA	☐
TMFFQ	☐

Question 2	
STRONG	☐
STURDY	☐
MIGHTY	☐
MANNER	☐
STREAM	☐

Question 3	
SMKDCT	☐
GZNEBD	☐
GAMVYD	☐
SVRTSG	☐
JDDFES	☐

Question 4	
WEVUMMZ	☐
GNERWWT	☐
WDUVMMZ	☐
GNDSXXK	☐
POUNNRZ	☐

Question 5	
MANAGED	☐
MORNING	☐
MADNESS	☐
MACHINE	☐
MAGNIFY	☐

Question 6	
FGIJHS	☐
WQASTW	☐
EIIJHO	☐
EIJJRP	☐
WRBRUX	☐

Question 7	
CRIMES	☐
OCCURS	☐
CROAKS	☐
HONEST	☐
OCCUPY	☐

Question 8	
READS	☐
REACH	☐
RELAY	☐
RETRY	☐
REPLY	☐

Question 9	
RUNNER	☐
PINCER	☐
PICKED	☐
HUNGRY	☐
HUNTER	☐

Question 10	
NHDZA	☐
XQNIJ	☐
XQNRK	☐
WPNJK	☐
XRNHI	☐

Question 11	
TFSLCH	☐
SFTLCH	☐
TFTMAG	☐
RZSLYF	☐
UETLCF	☐

Question 12	
SIGNS	☐
TIDES	☐
SIGHS	☐
YEARS	☐
TRIES	☐

Time Target:
12 minutes

Time Taken _____

Your score....

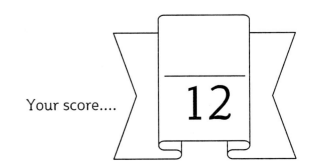

12

Word Formation

In the following questions there are three pairs of words. You must find the pattern and use it to complete the third pair in the same way as the first two pairs. Find the missing word and mark it on the multiple choice answer sheet.

For example: (spout, out)   (solid, lid)   (depot, **pot**)

1.   (tread, tea)   (shows, sow)   (tried,   )

2.   (slime, mile)   (scare, race)   (stone,   )

3.   (their, heir)   (thigh, high)   (those,   )

4.   (accent, neat)   (gauges, eggs)   (afford,   )

5.   (wand, wane)   (lass, last)   (fill,   )

6.   (extent, text)   (creams, ears)   (strains,   )

7.   (tombs, mob)   (tract, arc)   (trunk,   )

8.   (escape, cape)   (become, comb)   (embark,   )

9.   (might, night)   (cream, dream)   (block,   )

10.   (shame, mesh)   (atone, neat)   (arise,   )

11.   (burrows, rows)   (catwalk, talk)   (dormant,   )

12.   (breed, seed)   (clash, mash)   (sleek,   )

Your colour rating....

12

Question 1		Question 2		Question 3		Question 4		Question 5		Question 6	
red	☐	tone	☐	shoe	☐	ford	☐	fell	☐	rats	☐
tie	☐	note	☐	hose	☐	raft	☐	file	☐	star	☐
tea	☐	toes	☐	test	☐	road	☐	fall	☐	tins	☐
die	☐	sent	☐	shot	☐	off	☐	film	☐	airs	☐
ear	☐	near	☐	hots	☐	afro	☐	felt	☐	nits	☐

Question 7		Question 8		Question 9		Question 10		Question 11		Question 12	
nut	☐	bear	☐	blobs	☐	ears	☐	damn	☐	meek	☐
nun	☐	bare	☐	locks	☐	sear	☐	road	☐	male	☐
rut	☐	bark	☐	slack	☐	rear	☐	mant	☐	peek	☐
run	☐	kerb	☐	clock	☐	seas	☐	roam	☐	eels	☐
urn	☐	ream	☐	socks	☐	rise	☐	rant	☐	keep	☐

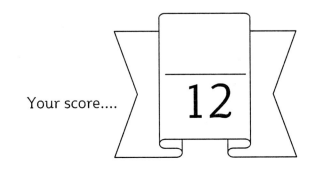

Time Target:
6 minutes

Time Taken _____

Your score.... **12**

Word Formation 2

In each of the following questions, the word in brackets is made using letters taken from the word outside the brackets. You must find the pattern for the first group of words and use it to complete the missing word from the second group in the same way. Find the missing word and mark it on the multiple choice answer sheet.

For example: night   (hate)   maple

comma (**meal**) peril

1. space   [read]   tired

    crate   [   ]   medal

2. agile   [align]   minds

    slams   [   ]   talks

3. fight   [leaf]   fable

    tripe   [   ]   filed

4. detail   [liar]   friend

    evades   [   ]   ceiling

5. screen   [crave]   loaves

    hopes   [   ]   ovens

6. collie   [lithe]   think

    demean [   ]   soaps

7. trail   [calm]   camel

    heart   [   ]   leeks

8. delays   [leans]   rented

    depots   [   ]   holds

9. beyond   [money]   mantle

    hatred   [   ]   crumbs

10. risked   [rigs]   bring

    hasten   [   ]   blows

11. prone   [nears]   artist

    crisp   [   ]   achieve

12. creates   [tears]   listens

    bedroom [   ]   biscuit

Your colour rating....

14

Question 1		Question 2		Question 3		Question 4		Question 5		Question 6	
ales	☐	alarm	☐	leap	☐	vile	☐	seeps	☐	needs	☐
teal	☐	smile	☐	edit	☐	dial	☐	opens	☐	maths	☐
seat	☐	salts	☐	rile	☐	sing	☐	coves	☐	mason	☐
deal	☐	small	☐	earl	☐	side	☐	shops	☐	means	☐
team	☐	malts	☐	epic	☐	line	☐	henna	☐	loans	☐

Question 7		Question 8		Question 9		Question 10		Question 11		Question 12	
late	☐	tools	☐	brush	☐	lash	☐	spire	☐	cores	☐
hate	☐	poles	☐	cream	☐	lass	☐	spies	☐	cares	☐
lets	☐	leant	☐	crust	☐	taps	☐	spear	☐	codes	☐
kite	☐	loads	☐	cause	☐	hole	☐	space	☐	crust	☐
last	☐	pools	☐	trust	☐	last	☐	spade	☐	combs	☐

Time Target:
9 minutes

Time Taken _____

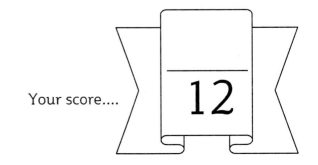

Your score....

12

Code Matching

In each of the questions below, there are four words and three codes. Each code matches one of the words, but they are not written in the right order. One of the words does not have a code. Work out the correct code for each word and then answer the questions that follow. Mark your answer on the multiple choice answer sheet provided.

DIRE   TAPE   HIDE   DEAD

6193   6356   7543

SILT   SEAS   SHIN   SAND

4386   4217   4524

1.   What is the code for DREAD?

2.   What does 459563 mean?

3.   What is the code for TRIPPED?

10.   What does 48216 mean?

11.   What is the code for DEALS?

12.   What does 155785 mean?

SACK   RICE   CURT   PEAR

7495   9376   8291

4.   What does 81476 mean?

5.   What is the code for CRASS?

6.   What does 649156 mean?

EAST   SAFE   TEAR   FANS

9476   2463   3245

7.   What is the code for FEET?

8.   What does 6472 mean?

9.   What is the code for FASTEN?

Your colour rating....

Question 1		Question 2		Question 3		Question 4		Question 5		Question 6	
69346	☐	TRADED	☐	5419963	☐	REARS	☐	96288	☐	TICKET	☐
69356	☐	SHADED	☐	7916645	☐	SKIRT	☐	54722	☐	STRUTS	☐
49354	☐	PARADE	☐	7911445	☐	SKIER	☐	54766	☐	TRACKS	☐
49294	☐	STARED	☐	5944361	☐	SCARE	☐	97288	☐	STICKS	☐
69436	☐	PARTIES	☐	7914436	☐	RACES	☐	85499	☐	CRACKS	☐

Question 7		Question 8		Question 9		Question 10		Question 11		Question 12	
3554	☐	NEAR	☐	946527	☐	LEADS	☐	97528	☐	READER	☐
2995	☐	SEAT	☐	326925	☐	SHINE	☐	72584	☐	NEEDLE	☐
9443	☐	SANE	☐	325926	☐	SEEDS	☐	75284	☐	LEADER	☐
2665	☐	NEED	☐	946327	☐	SLANT	☐	42857	☐	LEANED	☐
9223	☐	SITE	☐	246327	☐	ASHEN	☐	73157	☐	SNEERS	☐

Time Target:
9 minutes

Time Taken _____

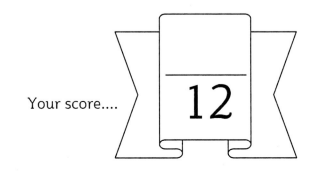

Your score....

12

Missing Letters

In each of the questions below, find one letter that will complete the word in front of the brackets and begin the word after the brackets. The same letter must fit into both sets of brackets. Mark your answer on the multiple choice answer sheet provided.

For example: CA (**T**) ALK   FLA (**T**) ALL

1.   SWIF (_) EAL, PLAN (_) IDY

2.   PLACI (_) ESPISE, TONE (_) OME

3.   REAC (_) ALL, MARS (_) OPES

4.   GRE (_) ELL, MELLO (_) AIL

5.   STOO (_) HONE, YEL (_) INTS

6.   CHES (_) HREWD, BAS (_) ELDOM

7.   PRIM (_) AST, FLUK (_) VENT

8.   SHOO (_) IN, FROC (_) NIGHT

9.   THUM (_) RICK, COM (_) OATS

10. SPOO (_) ANS, SUR (_) RUGAL

11. SPA (_) INETY, COLUM (_) APS

12. FEE (_) EED, LUCI (_) RASTIC

Your colour rating....

Question 1	
S	☐
T	☐
R	☐
W	☐
F	☐

Question 2	
S	☐
E	☐
R	☐
D	☐
H	☐

Question 3	
N	☐
T	☐
I	☐
R	☐
H	☐

Question 4	
W	☐
T	☐
Y	☐
C	☐
F	☐

Question 5	
L	☐
D	☐
S	☐
B	☐
P	☐

Question 6	
E	☐
H	☐
S	☐
U	☐
R	☐

Question 7	
N	☐
S	☐
Y	☐
A	☐
E	☐

Question 8	
B	☐
R	☐
T	☐
K	☐
P	☐

Question 9	
G	☐
T	☐
S	☐
B	☐
F	☐

Question 10	
D	☐
F	☐
K	☐
G	☐
E	☐

Question 11	
M	☐
T	☐
A	☐
N	☐
S	☐

Question 12	
O	☐
S	☐
A	☐
X	☐
D	☐

Time Target:
5 minutes

Time Taken _____

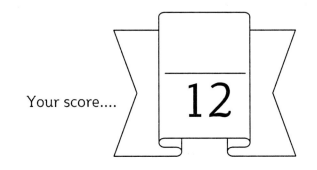

Your score....

12

Hidden Words

In each of the sentences below there is a four letter word which has been hidden at the end of one word and the beginning of the next. Find the pair of words that contain the hidden word and mark it on the answer sheet.

For example: Have you seen the tool**s and** paint? **= sand**

1. The arrow headed towards the target.

2. The woman drove into the garage.

3. Wouldn't Sally rather do drama today?

4. It was her plan, not mine!

5. What a pretty garden that is!

6. The gnome remained in the flowerbed.

7. Can you send the rest tonight?

8. Your tenant should pay his rent.

9. Please turn off the alarm now!

10. I love roast chicken on Sundays.

11. The lady's luggage was too heavy.

12. Is the cover blue or green?

Your colour rating....

Question 1	
The arrow	☐
arrow headed	☐
headed towards	☐
towards the	☐
the target	☐

Question 2	
The woman	☐
woman drove	☐
drove into	☐
into the	☐
the garage	☐

Question 3	
Wouldn't Sally	☐
Sally rather	☐
rather do	☐
do drama	☐
drama today	☐

Question 4	
It was	☐
was her	☐
her plan	☐
plan not	☐
not mine	☐

Question 5	
What a	☐
a pretty	☐
pretty garden	☐
garden that	☐
that is	☐

Question 6	
The gnome	☐
gnome remained	☐
remained in	☐
in the	☐
the flowerbed	☐

Question 7	
Can you	☐
you send	☐
send the	☐
the rest	☐
rest tonight	☐

Question 8	
Your tenant	☐
tenant should	☐
should pay	☐
pay his	☐
his rent	☐

Question 9	
Please turn	☐
turn off	☐
off the	☐
the alarm	☐
alarm now	☐

Question 10	
I love	☐
love roast	☐
roast chicken	☐
chicken on	☐
on Sundays	☐

Question 11	
The lady's	☐
lady's luggage	☐
luggage was	☐
was too	☐
too heavy	☐

Question 12	
Is the	☐
the cover	☐
cover blue	☐
blue or	☐
or green	☐

 Time Target:
5 minutes

Time Taken _____

Your score.... 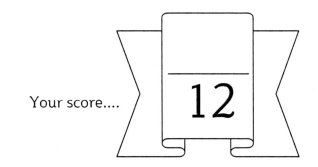 12

Transferring letters

In these questions, you must take one letter out of the word on the left and place it into the word on the right, making two new words. You can place the letter between any of the letters in the word on the right, but you can't rearrange the letters. Both new words must be spelled correctly.

When you have found the letter that can be moved, mark it on the answer sheet.

For example: CARD   RAW   (**D**)   CAR   DRAW

1.   shout   spot

2.   petal   ramp

3.   leans   rids

4.   bails   rush

5.   fibre   less

6.   drive   cubs

7.   start   roam

8.   grain   sins

9.   beast   tries

10.   lunge   spar

11.   scale   rest

12.   health   seas

Your colour rating....

Question 1	
S	☐
H	☐
O	☐
U	☐
T	☐

Question 2	
P	☐
E	☐
T	☐
A	☐
L	☐

Question 3	
L	☐
E	☐
A	☐
N	☐
S	☐

Question 4	
B	☐
A	☐
I	☐
L	☐
S	☐

Question 5	
F	☐
I	☐
B	☐
R	☐
E	☐

Question 6	
D	☐
R	☐
I	☐
V	☐
E	☐

Question 7	
S	☐
T	☐
A	☐
R	☐
T	☐

Question 8	
G	☐
R	☐
A	☐
I	☐
N	☐

Question 9	
B	☐
E	☐
A	☐
S	☐
T	☐

Question 10	
L	☐
U	☐
N	☐
G	☐
E	☐

Question 11	
S	☐
C	☐
A	☐
L	☐
E	☐

Question 12	
H	☐
E	☐
A	☐
L	☐
T	☐

Time Target:
6 minutes

Time Taken _____

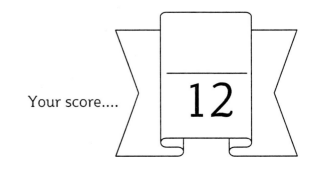

Your score....

12

Odd Ones Out

In these questions, three of the five words are related in some way. Find the **TWO** words that **DO NOT** go with these three and mark them **BOTH** on the answer sheet.

For example: knife   spoon   **plate**   **bowl**   fork

1.   hopeful optimistic pessimistic positive doubtful

2.   yard gram mass foot metre

3.   maple pancake willow pine wood

4.   peculiar persistent unusual strange commonplace

5.   slight gaunt slender obese plump

6.   tired feeble fatigued energetic exhausted

7.   cranberry banana raspberry strawberry lemon

8.   cabinet wardrobe desk sofa armchair

9.   copper metal lead concrete silver

10. painful soothe alleviate worsen relieve

11. obvious clear transparent apparent hidden

12. coarse course silk rough rugged

Your colour rating....

Question 1		Question 2		Question 3		Question 4		Question 5		Question 6	
hopeful	☐	yard	☐	maple	☐	peculiar	☐	slight	☐	tired	☐
optimistic	☐	gram	☐	pancake	☐	persistent	☐	gaunt	☐	feeble	☐
pessimistic	☐	mass	☐	willow	☐	unusual	☐	slender	☐	fatigued	☐
positive	☐	foot	☐	pine	☐	strange	☐	obese	☐	energetic	☐
doubtful	☐	metre	☐	wood	☐	common-place	☐	plump	☐	exhausted	☐

Question 7		Question 8		Question 9		Question 10		Question 11		Question 12	
cranberry	☐	cabinet	☐	copper	☐	painful	☐	obvious	☐	coarse	☐
banana	☐	wardrobe	☐	metal	☐	soothe	☐	clear	☐	course	☐
raspberry	☐	desk	☐	lead	☐	alleviate	☐	transparent	☐	silk	☐
strawberry	☐	sofa	☐	concrete	☐	worsen	☐	apparent	☐	rough	☐
lemon	☐	armchair	☐	silver	☐	relieve	☐	hidden	☐	rugged	☐

Time Target:
5 minutes

Time Taken _____

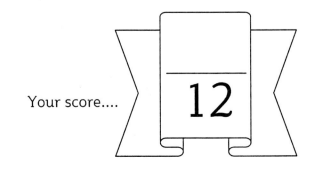

Your score.... 12

25

Synonyms

In these questions, find **TWO** words, **ONE** from each group, that are **CLOSEST IN MEANING**. Mark **BOTH WORDS** on the answer sheet.

For example: (**angry**   tired   smile)
            (yawn   face   **cross**)

1. (entice exhaustion youthful)
    (magic splendid lure)

2. (strong keen protection)
    (broken eager heavy)

3. (disappointed woe dramatic)
    (fortunate regal dejected)

4. (consequence prediction guilt)
    (remorse game cause)

5. (gloat speak impress)
    (stunning boast answer)

6. (mystery phantom mist)
    (ghost weather darkness)

7. (slice country saunter)
    (gallop stroll green)

8. (sincere letter original)
    (stamped genuine recent)

9. (hateful rely tremor)
    (argument queue depend)

10. (thin taunt package)
     (insult wrapping plump)

11. (percussion apt repulsive)
     (imitate vile useless)

12. (postpone schedule dairy)
     (notebook computer delay)

Your colour rating....

Question 1			
entice	☐	magic	☐
exhaustion	☐	splendid	☐
youthful	☐	lure	☐

Question 2			
strong	☐	broken	☐
keen	☐	eager	☐
protection	☐	heavy	☐

Question 3			
disappointed	☐	fortunate	☐
woe	☐	regal	☐
dramatic	☐	dejected	☐

Question 4			
consequence	☐	remorse	☐
prediction	☐	game	☐
guilt	☐	cause	☐

Question 5			
gloat	☐	stunning	☐
speak	☐	boast	☐
impress	☐	answer	☐

Question 6			
mystery	☐	ghost	☐
phantom	☐	weather	☐
mist	☐	darkness	☐

Question 7			
slice	☐	gallop	☐
country	☐	stroll	☐
saunter	☐	green	☐

Question 8			
sincere	☐	stamped	☐
letter	☐	genuine	☐
original	☐	recent	☐

Question 9			
hateful	☐	argument	☐
rely	☐	queue	☐
tremor	☐	depend	☐

Question 10			
thin	☐	insult	☐
taunt	☐	wrapping	☐
package	☐	plump	☐

Question 11			
percussion	☐	imitate	☐
apt	☐	vile	☐
repulsive	☐	useless	☐

Question 12			
postpone	☐	notebook	☐
schedule	☐	computer	☐
dairy	☐	delay	☐

Time Target:
5 minutes

Time Taken _____

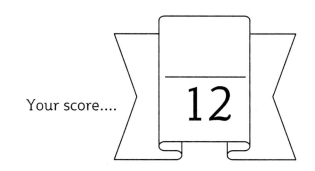

Your score.... 12

Antonyms

In each question below, find **TWO** words, **ONE** from each set of brackets that are the most **OPPOSITE IN MEANING**. Mark **BOTH WORDS** on the answer sheet.

For example: (black   night   **dark**)
                 (week   colour   **light**)

1.   (dishonest dissuade despise)
       (link encourage invalid)

2.   (door close screw)
       (tool measure distant)

3.   (complimentary excuse review)
       (free obey critical)

4.   (train assembly terminate)
       (commence leave taught)

5.   (prepared nimble melt)
       (inflexible gymnast potential)

6.   (describe detail detain)
       (revolve release respect)

7.   (condone invite propose)
       (condemn wedding guest)

8.   (wholesome significant consider)
       (irrelevant kind topical)

9.   (astute honest right)
       (test intelligent ignorant)

10.   (strong brief return)
      (weakness ticket long)

11.   (vault battle failure)
      (vanquish triumph valour)

12.   (wretched pathetic unworthy)
      (trust low cheerful)

Your colour rating....

Question 1

dishonest	☐	link	☐
dissuade	☐	encourage	☐
despise	☐	invalid	☐

Question 2

door	☐	tool	☐
close	☐	measure	☐
screw	☐	distant	☐

Question 3

complimentary	☐	free	☐
excuse	☐	obey	☐
review	☐	critical	☐

Question 4

train	☐	commence	☐
assembly	☐	leave	☐
terminate	☐	taught	☐

Question 5

prepared	☐	inflexible	☐
nimble	☐	gymnast	☐
melt	☐	potential	☐

Question 6

describe	☐	revolve	☐
detail	☐	release	☐
detain	☐	respect	☐

Question 7

condone	☐	condemn	☐
invite	☐	wedding	☐
propose	☐	guest	☐

Question 8

wholesome	☐	irrelevant	☐
significant	☐	kind	☐
consider	☐	topical	☐

Question 9

astute	☐	test	☐
honest	☐	intelligent	☐
right	☐	ignorant	☐

Question 10

strong	☐	weakness	☐
brief	☐	ticket	☐
return	☐	long	☐

Question 11

vault	☐	vanquish	☐
battle	☐	triumph	☐
failure	☐	valour	☐

Question 12

wretched	☐	trust	☐
pathetic	☐	low	☐
unworthy	☐	cheerful	☐

Time Target:
5 minutes

Time Taken _____

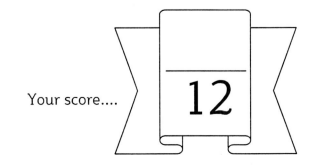

Your score.... 12

Compound Words

In each question below, underline **ONE** word from **BOTH** sets of brackets that together make a new word. The word from the top set of brackets always comes first. Mark **BOTH WORDS** on the answer sheet.

For example: (**flower** petal   tree)   (bark   soft   **pot**) = **flowerpot**

1. (walk   run   travel)
    (boat   led   tap)

2. (young   old   teen)
    (years   age   life)

3. (fore   under   for)
    (man   open   tolled)

4. (might   may   miss)
    (ore   or   not)

5. (reap   farm   sow)
    (pear   animal   lead)

6. (now   wed   can)
    (month   days   here)

7. (it   in   car)
    (excusable   fully   enter)

8. (miss   thin   mark)
    (king   take   correct)

9. (start   begin   end)
    (led   lead   follow)

10. (pig   washing   top)
    (garden   tail   lined)

11. (low   high   rob)
    (up   way   berry)

12. (gaunt   put   stop)
    (sign   right   let)

Your colour rating....

30

Question 1

walk	☐	boat	☐
run	☐	led	☐
travel	☐	tap	☐

Question 2

young	☐	years	☐
old	☐	age	☐
teen	☐	life	☐

Question 3

fore	☐	man	☐
under	☐	open	☐
for	☐	tolled	☐

Question 4

might	☐	ore	☐
may	☐	or	☐
miss	☐	not	☐

Question 5

reap	☐	pear	☐
farm	☐	animal	☐
sow	☐	lead	☐

Question 6

now	☐	month	☐
wed	☐	days	☐
can	☐	here	☐

Question 7

it	☐	excusable	☐
in	☐	fully	☐
car	☐	enter	☐

Question 8

miss	☐	king	☐
thin	☐	take	☐
mark	☐	correct	☐

Question 9

start	☐	led	☐
begin	☐	lead	☐
end	☐	follow	☐

Question 10

pig	☐	garden	☐
washing	☐	tail	☐
top	☐	lined	☐

Question 11

low	☐	up	☐
high	☐	way	☐
rob	☐	berry	☐

Question 12

gaunt	☐	sign	☐
put	☐	right	☐
stop	☐	let	☐

 Time Target:
5 minutes

Time Taken _____

Your score....

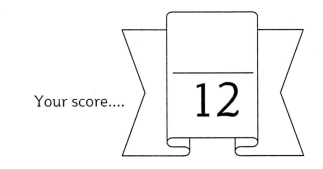

12

Complete the Word

The sentences below all have one word (in capitals) which has had three consecutive letters taken out. The three letters will make a correctly spelled word without changing the order. Find the three letter word which would complete the word in capitals and mark it on the answer sheet.

For example: The toolbox contained a **SNER.**   **PAN** *(SPANNER)*

1.   The children PREDED to be asleep.

2.   It had been so long, the man did not RENISE her.

3.   There are FR girls than boys in my class.

4.   The bird SED into the sky.

5.   The goal was DISALED by the referee.

6.   There are no SLES left in the stationery drawer.

7.   The new puppies were very PFUL.

8.   The picnic was ruined by a SM of bees.

9.   The cricket ball HURT towards the boundary.

10.   The boy was SUSDED from school for his behaviour.

11.   The girl has ADED a dog from a well-known charity.

12.   The drama teacher ALLOED the parts for the play.

Your colour

Question 1		Question 2		Question 3		Question 4		Question 5		Question 6	
ALE	☐	TOE	☐	EEL	☐	HER	☐	ALL	☐	APE	☐
END	☐	CON	☐	EWE	☐	LED	☐	LOW	☐	TIP	☐
TEN	☐	KIN	☐	TON	☐	ORE	☐	ALE	☐	TAP	☐
TIN	☐	COG	☐	FEW	☐	MEN	☐	OLD	☐	POT	☐
EAT	☐	LOT	☐	PIT	☐	OAR	☐	RED	☐	ADD	☐

Question 7		Question 8		Question 9		Question 10		Question 11		Question 12	
WIN	☐	YOU	☐	LAD	☐	PEN	☐	DIP	☐	GIN	☐
LIE	☐	WAR	☐	LET	☐	EAT	☐	OFF	☐	CAT	☐
LAY	☐	TIE	☐	LIT	☐	END	☐	MET	☐	KIT	☐
OUT	☐	ARM	☐	LED	☐	HEN	☐	NOW	☐	COT	☐
RAY	☐	PRY	☐	LOB	☐	PIN	☐	OPT	☐	WON	☐

Time Target:
9 minutes

Time Taken _____

Your score....

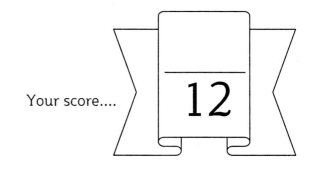

12

Homonyms

In each question below, there are two pairs of words. By looking at the multiple choice answer sheet, find the word that would go equally well with **BOTH** pairs and mark down your choice.

For example: (dance, party)   (globe, sphere) = **BALL**

1.   (ring, hoop)   (group, orchestra)

2.   (recent, topical)   (flow, movement)

3.   (shrink, diminish)   (document, agreement)

4.   (healthy, well)   (spasm, convulsion)

5.   (brain, mentality)   (care, disapprove)

6.   (modify, alter)   (coins, pennies)

7.   (argue, dispute)   (competition, tournament)

8.   (rubbish, waste)   (deny, decline)

9.   (flaw, imperfection)   (leave, abandon)

10.   (computer, system)   (comfort, reassure)

11.   (jump, leap)   (miss, disregard)

12.   (field, land)   (simple, modest)

Your colour rating....

Question 1		Question 2		Question 3		Question 4		Question 5		Question 6	
circle	☐	nowadays	☐	note	☐	slim	☐	worry	☐	cash	☐
band	☐	soon	☐	smaller	☐	fit	☐	consider	☐	pounds	☐
trio	☐	current	☐	decrease	☐	happy	☐	clever	☐	change	☐
sphere	☐	tide	☐	confident	☐	shake	☐	mind	☐	notes	☐
globe	☐	water	☐	contract	☐	tremor	☐	bright	☐	edit	☐

Question 7		Question 8		Question 9		Question 10		Question 11		Question 12	
fight	☐	reject	☐	fault	☐	toy	☐	omit	☐	green	☐
disobey	☐	refuse	☐	glitch	☐	console	☐	high	☐	humble	☐
disagree	☐	barren	☐	problem	☐	relieve	☐	skip	☐	garden	☐
contest	☐	decay	☐	defect	☐	game	☐	bounce	☐	boring	☐
heat	☐	rotten	☐	vacate	☐	sooth	☐	hurdle	☐	plain	☐

 Time Target:
5 minutes

Time Taken _____

Your score....

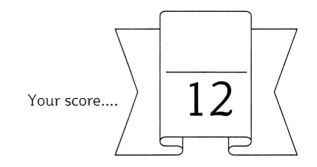

12

Sentence Analogies

In each of the questions below, find one word from each group that best completes the sentence. Mark **BOTH** words on the multiple choice answer sheet.

For example: Horse is to (race jump **stable**)
                as bee is to (swarm sky **hive**)

1.   Bicep is to (tricep arm muscle)
      as hamstring is to (farm stomach leg)

2.   Beef is to (Sunday calf cow)
      as bacon is to (pig pork breakfast)

3.   Brush is to (hair sweep bush)
      as drill is to (screwdriver dill mend)

4.   Gaunt is to (obese thin aunt)
      as collect is to (stamp charity distribute)

5.   Shoal is to (sea dolphin fish)
      as pack is to (wolves rabbits geese)

6.   Pound is to (weight money stone)
      as yard is to (tree metres distance)

7.   Slumber is to (party sleep birthday)
      as battle is to (sword soldier fight)

8.   Millennium is to (hundred thirty thousand)
      as decade is to (ten twelve twenty)

9.   Conifer is to (tree flower wood)
      as snapper is to (argument red fish)

10.   Lever is to (pull car revel)
      as ward is to (rewind draw play)

11.   So is to (soon why sew)
      as paced is to (paste walked tempo)

12.   Bachelor is to (life man servant)
      as spinster is to (clothes wheel woman)

Your colour rating....

36

Question 1

tricep	☐	farm	☐
arm	☐	stomach	☐
muscle	☐	leg	☐

Question 2

Sunday	☐	pig	☐
calf	☐	pork	☐
cow	☐	breakfast	☐

Question 3

hair	☐	screwdriver	☐
sweep	☐	dill	☐
bush	☐	mend	☐

Question 4

obese	☐	stamp	☐
thin	☐	charity	☐
aunt	☐	distribute	☐

Question 5

sea	☐	wolves	☐
dolphin	☐	rabbits	☐
fish	☐	geese	☐

Question 6

weight	☐	tree	☐
money	☐	metres	☐
stone	☐	distance	☐

Question 7

party	☐	sword	☐
sleep	☐	soldier	☐
birthday	☐	fight	☐

Question 8

hundred	☐	ten	☐
thirty	☐	twelve	☐
thousand	☐	twenty	☐

Question 9

tree	☐	argument	☐
flower	☐	red	☐
wood	☐	fish	☐

Question 10

pull	☐	rewind	☐
car	☐	draw	☐
revel	☐	play	☐

Question 11

soon	☐	paste	☐
why	☐	walked	☐
sew	☐	tempo	☐

Question 12

life	☐	clothes	☐
man	☐	wheel	☐
servant	☐	woman	☐

 Time Target:
5 minutes

Time Taken _____

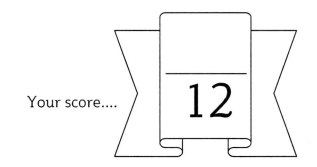

Your score.... 12

Algebra

In each question below, letters stand for numbers. Work out the answer to the sum and mark its **LETTER** on the multiple choice answer sheet.

For example: A = 4, B = 8, C = 2, D = 10, E = 18

$$A \times C + D = \textbf{E}$$

1. If A = 5, B = 4, C = 7, D = 1, E = 13

$$(A \times B) - C = \_\_\_\_$$

2. If A = 45, B = 11, C = 1, D = 4, E = 46

$$(D \times B) + C = \_\_\_\_$$

3. If A = 16, B = 10, C = 8, D = 2, E = 20

$$E - B + C - D = \_\_\_\_$$

4. If A = 12, B = 7, C = 15, D = 10, E = 5

$$(C + D) \div E = \_\_\_\_$$

5. If A = 33, B = 3, C = 11, D = 24, E = 8

$$A \div C \times E = \_\_\_\_$$

6. If A = 8, B = 4, C = 2, D = 6, E = 12

$$(C \times D \times A) \div E = \_\_\_\_$$

7. If A = 49, B = 4, C = 2, D = 3, E = 7

$$(B + D) \times E = \_\_\_\_$$

8. If A = 2, B = 35, C = 14, D = 5, E = 28

$$(B - E) \times A = \_\_\_\_$$

9. If A = 150, B = 12, C = 2, D = 9 E = 10

$$(A \div E + D) \div B = \_\_\_\_$$

10. If A = 9, B = 6, C = 3, D = 4, E = 8

$$(C \times B \times D) \div E = \_\_\_\_$$

11. If A = 56, B = 3, C = 8, D = 21, E = 64

$$D \div B \times C = \_\_\_\_$$

12. If A = 43, B = 8, C = 59, D = 6, E = 12

$$(A + C - D) \div E = \_\_\_\_$$

Your colour rating....

Question 1		Question 2		Question 3		Question 4		Question 5		Question 6	
A	☐	A	☐	A	☐	A	☐	A	☐	A	☐
B	☐	B	☐	B	☐	B	☐	B	☐	B	☐
C	☐	C	☐	C	☐	C	☐	C	☐	C	☐
D	☐	D	☐	D	☐	D	☐	D	☐	D	☐
E	☐	E	☐	E	☐	E	☐	E	☐	E	☐

Question 7		Question 8		Question 9		Question 10		Question 11		Question 12	
A	☐	A	☐	A	☐	A	☐	A	☐	A	☐
B	☐	B	☐	B	☐	B	☐	B	☐	B	☐
C	☐	C	☐	C	☐	C	☐	C	☐	C	☐
D	☐	D	☐	D	☐	D	☐	D	☐	D	☐
E	☐	E	☐	E	☐	E	☐	E	☐	E	☐

Time Target:
6 minutes

Time Taken _____

Your score....

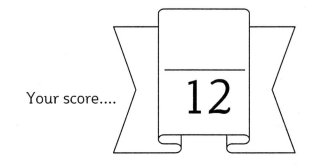

12

Number Sequences

In each question, find the number that continues the sequence in the best way and mark it on the multiple choice answer sheet.

For example: 15,   25,   35,   45,   55,   **65**

1.   10, 18, 26, 34, 42, 50

2.   22, 18, 26, 17, 30, 16, 34

3.   4, 5, 7, 10, 14, 19, 25

4.   6, 11, 21, 41, 81

5.   50, 40, 55, 45, 60, 50, 65

6.   36, 35, 29, 38, 22, 41, 15

7.   880, 440, 220, 110

8.   13, 8, 21, 16, 29, 24, 37

9.   4, 12, 36, 108

10. 97, 87, 78, 70, 63, 57

11. 42, 24, 36, 30, 30, 36, 24

12. 6, 14, 30, 62

Your colour rating....

Question 1		Question 2		Question 3		Question 4		Question 5		Question 6	
66	☐	55	☐	31	☐	141	☐	45	☐	10	☐
58	☐	34	☐	32	☐	121	☐	50	☐	43	☐
48	☐	20	☐	33	☐	164	☐	55	☐	9	☐
59	☐	15	☐	29	☐	101	☐	75	☐	42	☐
50	☐	14	☐	30	☐	161	☐	65	☐	44	☐

Question 7		Question 8		Question 9		Question 10		Question 11		Question 12	
50	☐	45	☐	340	☐	52	☐	52	☐	120	☐
52	☐	32	☐	430	☐	50	☐	18	☐	122	☐
55	☐	44	☐	332	☐	47	☐	28	☐	124	☐
60	☐	31	☐	348	☐	37	☐	42	☐	126	☐
65	☐	25	☐	324	☐	57	☐	44	☐	128	☐

Time Target:
6 minutes

Time Taken _____

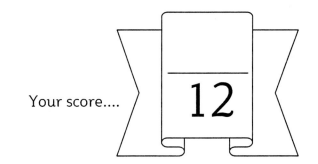

Your score....

12

Balancing Equations

For each of the questions below, find the missing number that completes the sum.

For example: $10 + 20 + 4 = 40 - 5 - (\underline{\mathbf{1}})$

1. $35 \div 5 \times 3 = 50 - 30 + (\quad)$

2. $14 + 7 + 11 = 40 \div 10 \times (\quad)$

3. $63 + 6 - 40 = 2 \times 5 + (\quad)$

4. $6 \times 7 + 10 = 100 - 59 + (\quad)$

5. $63 \div 7 - 3 = 24 + 24 \div (\quad)$

6. $130 \div 10 \times 2 = 57 - 22 - (\quad)$

7. $5 \times 8 - 22 = 10 + 26 \div (\quad)$

8. $6 \times 6 + 22 = 3 \times 9 + (\quad)$

9. $36 \div 4 \times 3 = 32 \times 2 - (\quad)$

10. $100 \div 4 \times 3 = 20 \times 3 + (\quad)$

11. $132 \div 12 - 2 = 150 \div 30 + (\quad)$

12. $11 \times 7 + 38 = 106 - 18 + (\quad)$

Your colour rating....

Question 1		Question 2		Question 3		Question 4		Question 5		Question 6	
11	☐	8	☐	13	☐	15	☐	12	☐	9	☐
1	☐	4	☐	14	☐	24	☐	8	☐	13	☐
2	☐	7	☐	18	☐	17	☐	7	☐	21	☐
6	☐	12	☐	19	☐	11	☐	3	☐	8	☐
9	☐	6	☐	12	☐	63	☐	9	☐	6	☐

Question 7		Question 8		Question 9		Question 10		Question 11		Question 12	
5	☐	30	☐	27	☐	10	☐	6	☐	27	☐
10	☐	29	☐	37	☐	19	☐	4	☐	20	☐
2	☐	31	☐	42	☐	17	☐	18	☐	26	☐
4	☐	33	☐	50	☐	15	☐	22	☐	36	☐
1	☐	32	☐	25	☐	20	☐	5	☐	28	☐

Time Target:
6 minutes

Time Taken _____

Your score....

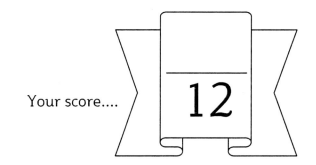

12

Relating Numbers

In each of the questions below, the numbers in the third set of brackets must be related to each other in the same way as in the first two sets of brackets. Find the missing number for each question and mark it on the multiple choice answer sheet.

For example: (10 (17) 7)   (14 (25) 11)   (8 (<u>15</u>) 7)

1.   (35 (5) 7)   (48 (3) 16)   (100 (   ) 4)

2.   (33 (81) 48)   (52 (153) 101)   (79 (   ) 35)

3.   (6 (36) 12)   (5 (25) 10)   (8 (   ) 8)

4.   (4 (21) 7)   (9 (36) 17)   (13 (   ) 20)

5.   (19 (15) 5)   (33 (28) 6)   (42 (   ) 10)

6.   (45 (15) 9)   (30 (13) 10)   (28 (   ) 4)

7.   (3 (14) 3)   (5 (35) 6)   (10 (   ) 9)

8.   (15 (6) 6)   (40 (26) 11)   (25 (   ) 12)

9.   (21 (31) 5)   (11 (25) 7)   (15 (   ) 10)

10.   (3 (27) 6)   (4 (24) 2)   (5 (   ) 3)

11.   (27 (4) 13)   (58 (8) 22)   (63 (   ) 67)

12.   (36 (98) 13)   (29 (106) 24)   (34 (   ) 21)

Your colour rating....

Question 1		Question 2		Question 3		Question 4		Question 5		Question 6	
15	☐	114	☐	42	☐	33	☐	63	☐	10	☐
25	☐	115	☐	34	☐	42	☐	33	☐	12	☐
20	☐	113	☐	38	☐	43	☐	13	☐	15	☐
30	☐	124	☐	32	☐	39	☐	27	☐	17	☐
400	☐	103	☐	30	☐	57	☐	32	☐	22	☐

Question 7		Question 8		Question 9		Question 10		Question 11		Question 12	
100	☐	13	☐	25	☐	48	☐	70	☐	56	☐
90	☐	10	☐	35	☐	40	☐	80	☐	55	☐
95	☐	16	☐	27	☐	32	☐	11	☐	112	☐
85	☐	19	☐	40	☐	30	☐	13	☐	118	☐
80	☐	23	☐	150	☐	64	☐	12	☐	110	☐

Time Target:
9 minutes

Time Taken _____

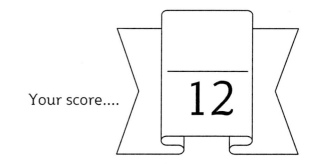

Your score....

12

45

Word Problems

Read the information for each question carefully, then find the correct answer and mark it on the answer sheet provided. You may be asked to mark down more than one answer for each question.

1. Luke's mum is 6 times the age Luke was a year ago. If she is 42, how old is Luke now?

    _____

2. Andrew, Samia and Simon are eating breakfast. They all have a slice of toast, but Samia and Andrew also have cereal whilst Simon eats scrambled eggs. Samia and Simon each finish with a pancake, whilst Andrew eats an apple and a pear.

    Which of the following statements MUST be true?

    A.   Simon eats more toast than Andrew.
    B.   Andrew doesn't like pancakes.
    C.   Simon eats less items than Andrew.
    D.   Andrew eats 3 items.
    E.   Samia eats the fewest items.

    _____

3. Mark leaves school at 15.50. His journey takes 25 minutes longer than Jake, who leaves school at 16.00 and gets home at 16.15. Josh arrives at home 20 minutes after Mark. What time does he get home?

    _____

4. 5 cars are competing in a race. The purple car finishes two positions behind the green car, but beats the white car. The blue comes 4th, two places behind the red car. The white car is the slowest.

    Who is in 3rd place?

    _____

5. Jane is on her way to a theme park. The journey should take 4 ½ hours, but she was 20 minutes later than expected. She left a quarter of an hour before 8.45am. What time did she arrive?

    _____

6. Lisa is three times Lauren's age, who will be 7 in two years time. Lucy is four years younger than Lisa. How old is Lucy?

    _____

7. Neil has 20 ties. 4 have green and blue stripes, 5 have pink and purple stripes, 7 are plain blue and the rest are grey with blue spots. How many ties have the colour blue on them?

    _____

8. Jack's birthday is on the 4th of August, but he decide to have his birthday party 13 days beforehand. Wha date is his birthday party?

    _____

9. Emily's watch is 9 minutes fast. It takes her 15 minutes to eat her tea. What is the real time she finishes her tea, if she started eating when her watch said 17.30?

    _____

10. 5 fruits are lined up on the kitchen counter. The kiw is second from the end and to the right of the middle fruit which is a pear. The fruits on either end are a nectarine and a peach. The apple is to the right of t nectarine.

    Which fruit is furthest left?

    _____

Question 1	
5	☐
8	☐
7	☐
11	☐
14	☐

Question 2	
A	☐
B	☐
C	☐
D	☐
E	☐

Question 3	
16.50	☐
16.40	☐
16.25	☐
16.45	☐
16.10	☐

Question 4	
Purple	☐
Green	☐
White	☐
Blue	☐
Red	☐

Question 5	
13.35	☐
13.20	☐
13.25	☐
14.10	☐
13.45	☐

Question 6	
12	☐
10	☐
15	☐
11	☐
16	☐

Question 7	
9	☐
15	☐
4	☐
11	☐
8	☐

Question 8	
22nd July	☐
19th July	☐
21st July	☐
28th July	☐
25th July	☐

Question 9	
17.33	☐
17.55	☐
17.36	☐
17.45	☐
17.54	☐

Question 10	
Kiwi	☐
Pear	☐
Nectarine	☐
Peach	☐
Apple	☐

Keep going.... There's more over the page!

11. Kirsty, Karen, Kelly, Kieran and Keith arrange
themselves from left to right in alphabetical order.

Who is in the middle?

_____

12. David, Jack, Jordan, Stephen and Becky are picking
strawberries.

Stephen picked twice as many as Becky, who picked 6
less than Jack, who picked 18. Jordan picked 10 more
than Stephen, but 5 less than David.

How many strawberries did Jordan pick?

_____

Your colour rating....

Question 11			Question 12	
Kirsty	☐		24	☐
Karen	☐		30	☐
Kelly	☐		37	☐
Kieran	☐		45	☐
Keith	☐		34	☐

Time Limit:
15 minutes

Time Taken _____

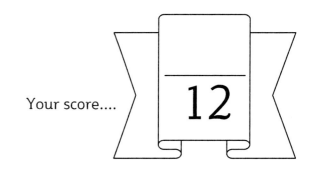

Your score....

12

Code Revision Questions - Answers

Letter Sequences	Letter Analogies	Code Words	Word Formation	Word Formation 2	Code Matching
1. MX	1. SE	1. UNGGRA	1. tie	1. deal	1. 69356
2. CO	2. OV	2. STURDY	2. note	2. small	2. PARADE
3. UR	3. VC	3. SVRTSG	3. hose	3. edit	3. 7914436
4. AW	4. IS	4. WDUVMMZ	4. road	4. side	4. SKIRT
5. UE	5. LV	5. MADNESS	5. film	5. opens	5. 97288
6. XM	6. UJ	6. EIIJHO	6. rats	6. mason	6. TICKET
7. UV	7. EI	7. OCCURS	7. urn	7. late	7. 9223
8. LK	8. CQ	8. REACH	8. bare	8. pools	8. SANE
9. FM	9. WU	9. HUNGRY	9. clock	9. crust	9. 946327
10. ER	10. BZ	10. XQNIJ	10. sear	10. lass	10. SLANT
11. YN	11. SX	11. TFSLCH	11. rant	11. space	11. 75284
12. IZ	12. KI	12. SIGHS	12. meek	12. cores	12. NEEDLE

Vocabulary Revision Questions - Answers

Missing Letters	Hidden Words	Transferring Letters	Odd Ones Out	Synonyms	
1. T	1. The arrow (hear)	1. U	1. pessimistic, doubtful	1. entice, lure	
2. D	2. drove into (vein)	2. T	2. gram, mass	2. keen, eager	
3. H	3. rather do (herd)	3. A	3. pancake, wood	3. disappointed, dejected	
4. W	4. was her (wash)	4. B	4. persistent, commonplace	4. guilt, remorse	
5. P	5. garden that (dent)	5. B	5. obese, plump	5. gloat, boast	
6. S	6. gnome remained (mere)	6. R	6. feeble, energetic	6. phantom, ghost	
7. E	7. the rest (here)	7. S	7. banana, lemon	7. saunter, stroll	
8. K	8. tenant should (ants)	8. G	8. sofa, armchair	8. sincere, genuine	
9. B	9. the alarm (heal)	9. B	9. metal, concrete	9. rely, depend	
10. F	10. love roast (over)	10. E	10. painful, worsen	10. taunt, insult	
11. N	11. lady's luggage (slug)	11. C	11. transparent, hidden	11. repulsive, vile	
12. D	12. cover blue (verb)	12. L	12. course, silk	12. postpone, delay	

Antonyms	Compound Words	Complete The Word	Homonyms	Sentence Analogies	
1. dissuade, encourage	1. travel/led	1. TEN	1. band	1. arm, leg	
2. close, distant	2. teen/age	2. COG	2. current	2. cow, pig	
3. complimentary, critical	3. fore/man	3. EWE	3. contract	3. bush, dill	
4. terminate, commence	4. may/or	4. OAR	4. fit	4. obese, distribute	
5. nimble, inflexible	5. reap/pear	5. LOW	5. mind	5. fish, wolves	
6. detain, release	6. now/here	6. TAP	6. change	6. weight, distance	
7. condone, condemn	7. in/excusable	7. LAY	7. contest	7. sleep, fight	
8. significant, irrelevant	8. thin/king	8. WAR	8. refuse	8. thousand, ten	
9. astute, ignorant	9. start/led	9. LED	9. defect	9. tree, fish	
10. brief, long	10. pig/tail	10. PEN	10. console	10. revel, draw	
11. failure, triumph	11. high/way	11. OPT	11. skip	11. sew, paste	
12. wretched, cheerful	12. gaunt/let	12. CAT	12. plain	12. man, woman	

Maths Revision Questions - Answers

Algebra	Number Sequences	Balancing Equations	Relating Numbers	Word Problems
1. E	1. 58	1. 1	1. 25	1. 8
2. A	2. 15	2. 8	2. 114	2. C
3. A	3. 32	3. 19	3. 32	3. 16.50
4. E	4. 161	4. 11	4. 43	4. Purple
5. D	5. 55	5. 8	5. 33	5. 13.20
6. A	6. 44	6. 9	6. 17	6. 11
7. A	7. 55	7. 2	7. 95	7. 15
8. C	8. 32	8. 31	8. 10	8. 22nd July
9. C	9. 324	9. 37	9. 35	9. 17.36
10. A	10. 52	10. 15	10. 40	10. Nectarine
11. A	11. 42	11. 4	11. 13	11. Kelly
12. B	12. 126	12. 27	12. 110	12. 34